"Magical book that encourages kids to pursue their dreams."
— *Craig Webster, German National Coach and coach of Stefi Graf*

"The tips in this book will be useful to all intense competitors. Nerves and anxiety are the most common problems of nearly everyone involved in sports. Severe self criticism is almost universal among athletes."
— *John Poarch, Psychiatrist*

"A whimsical, fun adventure of child empowerment!"
— *J.R. Becker, Best-selling author of the Annabelle & Aiden children's book series*

"Our mental skills are the foundation for everything that we experience in this world. This book exposes children to the mental skills they should consider to perform at their best on and off the tennis court."
— *Dave Mullins, Mental Performance Coach and former NCAA Division 1 Coach*

"A fun and creative book. It inspires young athletes to be the best they can be."
— *Gracie Epps, U.S. National Junior champion*

D1313805

Dear Reader,

Growing up playing tennis I faced some hard competition on the court. In addition to the sun, wind, and my opponent, my biggest competitor was me. Once I figured out how to incorporate mental toughness strategies, I played with more ease than ever before. It is my hope that my tips and book will help you in your journey to finding the zone and becoming the best you can be.

Sincerely,
Kobe Nhin

ISBN 978-1-7338627-1-4
Cataloging in Publication Data Library of Congress Control number: 2019938344
First published May 2019
www.kobenhin.com

HOW TO WIN WIMBLEDON IN PAJAMAS

This book is dedicated to my mom and dad
who taught me how to believe.

Grow Grit Press

Hi, my name is Will.
Wimbledon is very hard to win,
but I won it in pajamas.

And that's why,
I'm giving 5 tips on how to win
Wimbledon in your pajamas.

So here they are.

Tip 1: Be as **Carefree** as a bird in the wind. You can even wear your pajamas.

Any pajamas will work.

Blue and white striped ones.
Pajamas with bananas on them.
Or even panda pajamas.
It doesn't really matter what you choose.

Tip 2: Find your motivation.
If you can, walk to a tennis court.
But if you can't, don't worry.
Any wall will do.
Even your grassy front yard.
Or a driveway.

Once you find your spot,
breathe in the cool, crisp air.
Now ask yourself this question,
"Why do I want to win Wimbledon?"
For the money,
for the fame,
or to get better?

(Trust me, you'll want a good
reason to push you through
when things get tough.)

Tip 3: Maintain a laser-like FOCUS.
When you start playing,
don't let your brothers, parents,
or neighbors bother you.

You'll want to choose a ritual.
Play with your strings.

Even dry off with a hand towel.
You can also pick your butt.
You'll want to perform the
same ritual after every point.

Tip 4: When you're playing tennis,
confidence is key.
So hit the ball as freely as you can.
Let it go over the moon if it wants to!

Imagine yourself playing the match.
Visualize what shots and strategies
you'll use to move your opponent.

Feel the ball.
See the yellow fuzz come off.
Listen to the POP when it hits
the sweet spot on your racket.

Tip 5: Stay **Calm** when the crowd cheers or when you get nervous.

Don't get distracted by
your own thoughts, bees,
or even flying acrobats.

Talk to yourself.
No it's not weird.
Say positive things to yourself like,

"You got this!"

You'll want to think about
the next point and only the next point.

If you do this, you won't get nervous.

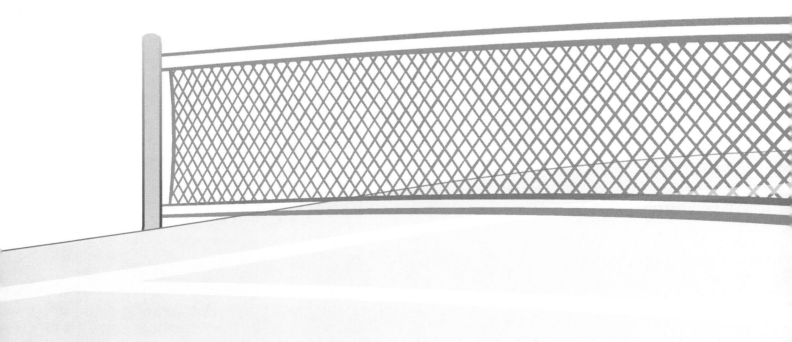

After you win Wimbledon,
you'll want to give your speech.
Thank the people who have
helped you along the way.

Just laugh.
Talk excitedly.
Smile.

Now just one more thing before you leave.
Take off your shoes.
Feel the sleek, cold grass with your bare feet.

You'll want to remember this feeling forever.

Grow Grit Press Mission Statement

Encourage a growth mindset: We believe it is important for kids to develop intrinsic motivation and autonomy through the development of long-term goals. Setting our sights on performance goals, rather than outcome goals provide a basis for grit and perseverance. We hope these books give children a love for battling new challenges and that they grow up eager to explore what this big, beautiful world has to offer.

Cultivate kids' self-confidence: We believe it is important for kids to learn how to practice positive self-talk. The more they understand that even mistakes and failures teach us, the more they can focus on celebrating their journey, mistakes and all. Our books will teach kids to be courageous enough to take risks and trust that the dots will someday connect. We want to teach kids how it feels to be scared and brave all at once, and how to move past fear and learn to jump.

Increase kids' focus and attention: We all get side-tracked and that's why it's important to have rituals to reset oneself. Our hope is that these stories will help kids get back on track and focus on the task at hand. Life itself is overwhelming. We want to help kids see that everyone faces hurdles and that we can stay focused with habits and mantras.

Develop perseverance and grit: Setbacks and failures teach us how to be graceful in the face of adversity. The books aim to encourage diligence and a hard work ethic.

About the Authors

Kobe Nhin

Kobe loves to hang out with his brothers and dog, Bacon. He is a member of the National Junior Honor Society. Kobe is inspired to write to help others overcome any negative self beliefs that may hinder their growth as it did his. He has learned to develop a storm-chasing mindset, always looking for obstacles to overcome.

For lesson plans, visit **www.KobeNhin.com** and sign up for new book releases. Follow him on social media **f** **@MentalToughnessTips** **@GrowGrit**

Mary Nhin

Mary loves being the guinea pig for all her husband, Kang's kitchen creations. She is a mom of 3 boys, wife of 23 years, business/life coach, and author. For 20 years, she and Kang have been enriching people's lives through their companies Nhinja and Grow Grit Press. She has been awarded the Forty under 40 and Inc. 5000.

For lesson plans, visit **www.MaryNhin.com** and sign up for new book releases. Follow her on social media **f** **@marynhin** **@marynhin**

Mental Toughness Growth Plan

I rate myself the following: 1-10 (10 is best)

	Today's Date:	Goal Date:
Example	6	9
Confidence		
Calm		
Carefree		
Motivated		
Focused		

Techniques I'm good at:

_____
_____
_____
_____
_____
_____

Techniques I want to improve:

_____
_____
_____
_____
_____
_____

Notes:

_____
_____
_____
_____
_____
_____

Positive Self-Talk

I am strong, confident and calm when I compete.
I can and will reach my highest goals.
I love to compete.

I use rituals.
I believe in myself and that I can reach my dreams.

Can you think of some more? Write them down here.

_____

_____

_____

_____

Rituals

Towel off between points.   Bounce on balls of your toes.   Play with your strings.

What rituals can you think of?

_____

_____

_____

_____

Mantras

Next point!   Right here!   Let's do this!   Deep and heavy!   Fast feet!

What mantras can you think of?

_____

_____

_____

_____

Long-Term Goals (Motivation)

What's your long term goals?

_____
_____
_____
_____

What would be the worst thing that could happen if you didn't achieve this?

_____
_____
_____
_____

Number and list some short-term goals.

_____
_____
_____
_____

Now number and list an exercise or task that you could do on a regular basis for you to reach each short-term goal.

_____
_____
_____
_____

47887134R00024

Made in the USA
Lexington, KY
13 August 2019